Large Print
Color by Number
Coloring Book
for Adults

Volume 2
A Variety of Simple,
Easy Designs for Relaxation

Copyright © 2021

Our Color Palette Tips

1. **Colors corresponding to each number are shown on the back cover of the book - NEW- There are only 25 colors total in this book, with one "Flesh Tone" color where you can choose any flesh tone!**
Each number corresponds to a color shown on the back of the book. **There will sometimes be an asterisk (*) that corresponds to "Any Flesh Tone."**
To the left of each image, there's a list of colors used within that particular image. Simply match the numbers on the images to the colors on the list. If you tear a page out of the book, you can simply use the color key on the back of the book to match your colors. If you don't have an exact color match, that's totally fine. Feel free to use a similar color or shade. Although this is a color by number book, it's completely okay to get creative and change up the colors listed. You can let your imagination run wild, and color the images with whichever colors you like and have. The numbers are here to be a guide and to allow you to color without having to focus your energy on choosing colors.

2. **If there are any spaces on an image without a number, you can go ahead and leave that space white (blank)**
You can leave any space without a number white (blank), or you can fill that space in with any color you like. Another idea is to color that space in with a white color (for example, if you'd like to use a shiny white or a different shade of white on an image.)

3. **Bonus Images may have a slightly different color palette**
Because the bonus images are from previous books with slightly different color palettes, they may include colors that aren't on the back of this book. Simply match them the best that you can, or choose completely different colors if you like. You are the artist and you are allowed to relax and enjoy!

Color By Number Tips

1. Relax and have fun

Let your cares slip away as you color the images. Take your time. Coloring is a meditative activity and there's no wrong way to do it. Feel free to color as you listen to music, watch TV, lounge in bed- do whatever relaxes you most! You can also color while you're out and about- on the train or at a cafe- take the book with you anywhere you go. Coloring is therapeutic and is great for stress relief and relaxation!

2. Choose your coloring tools

Everyone has their favorite coloring markers, crayons, pencils, pens- even paints! Feel free to color with any tool that you like! If you choose markers or paints, we recommend putting a blank sheet of paper or cardboard behind each image, so that your colors don't run onto the next image.

3. Test out your colors

Feel free to test out your colors on our Color Test Sheets at the back, and use our Custom Color Chart to make the color choices your own!

Relax and Enjoy!

Love Color By Number?
We'd love to see your beautiful work!
Feel free to share your images
from this book, or any of our other books,
to our Facebook page!
Facebook: bit.ly/FBQuestopia

And follow us on Instagram for flip throughs of new books!
Instagram: @ColorQuestopia
(please tag us if you post any of our drawings you've colored-
we'd love to see them!)

Also, feel free to email us your colored drawings and
we'll share some of them for you!

Email: questopiacolor@gmail.com

4. Brown

6. Tan

8. Red

10. Orange

12. Yellow

17. Aqua Green

18. Light Blue

19. Blue

23. Pink

2. Gray

4. Brown

5. Dark Brown

6. Tan

7. Peach

8. Red

10. Orange

12. Yellow

14. Light Green

15. Green

19. Blue

21. Lilac

22. Violet

23. Pink

24. Vivid Pink

1. Black

8. Red

10. Orange

20. Dark Blue

21. Lilac

22. Violet

24. Vivid Pink

1. Black

4. Brown

5. Dark Brown

6. Tan

12. Yellow

15. Green

23. Pink

7. Peach

8. Red

10. Orange

12. Yellow

14. Light Green

17. Aqua Green

20. Dark Blue

22. Violet

24. Vivid Pink

4. Brown

7. Peach

8. Red

10. Orange

12. Yellow

14. Light Green

15. Green

16. Dark Green

19. Blue

20. Dark Blue

21. Lilac

22. Violet

23. Pink

24. Vivid Pink

4. Brown

8. Red

10. Orange

11. Light Yellow

12. Yellow

14. Light Green

15. Green

16. Dark Green

19. Blue

20. Dark Blue

23. Pink

24. Vivid Pink

4. Brown

6. Tan

7. Peach

8. Red

12. Yellow

13. Golden Yellow

15. Green

17. Aqua Green

18. Light Blue

22. Violet

23. Pink

2. Gray

4. Brown

8. Red

10. Orange

12. Yellow

14. Light Green

15. Green

16. Dark Green

22. Violet

4. Brown

8. Red

10. Orange

12. Yellow

15. Green

18. Light Blue

19. Blue

20. Dark Blue

22. Violet

23. Pink

24. Vivid Pink

8. **Red**

10. **Orange**

12. **Yellow**

15. **Green**

17. **Aqua Green**

18. **Light Blue**

20. **Dark Blue**

23. **Pink**

24. **Vivid Pink**

6. Tan

7. Peach

8. Red

10. Orange

12. Yellow

14. Light Green

15. Green

17. Aqua Green

18. Light Blue

20. Dark Blue

23. Pink

24. Vivid Pink

1. Black

2. Gray

3. Dark Gray

10. Orange

17. Aqua Green

18. Light Blue

22. Violet

1. Black

8. Red

10. Orange

12. Yellow

15. Green

17. Aqua Green

20. Dark Blue

24. Vivid Pink

1. Black

4. Brown

5. Dark Brown

6. Tan

8. Red

10. Orange

12. Yellow

15. Green

17. Aqua Green

18. Light Blue

20. Dark Blue

1. Black

6. Tan

8. Red

9. Orange Red

10. Orange

12. Yellow

15. Green

17. Aqua Green

18. Light Blue

20. Dark Blue

21. Lilac

23. Pink

24. Vivid Pink

1. **Black**

6. **Tan**

7. **Peach**

8. **Red**

9. **Orange Red**

12. **Yellow**

15. **Green**

19. **Blue**

22. **Violet**

23. **Pink**

24. **Vivid Pink**

2. Gray

3. Dark Gray

4. Brown

5. Dark Brown

12. Yellow

14. Light Green

15. Green

16. Dark Green

18. Light Blue

19. Blue

4. Brown

8. Red

10. Orange

12. Yellow

15. Green

16. Dark Green

17. Aqua Green

18. Light Blue

19. Blue

20. Dark Blue

23. Pink

1. Black

4. Brown

5. Dark Brown

6. Tan

7. Peach

8. Red

9. Orange Red

10. Orange

12. Yellow

14. Light Green

15. Green

16. Dark Green

19. Blue

21. Lilac

22. Violet

23. Pink

24. Vivid Pink

2. Gray

3. Dark Gray

4. Brown

6. Tan

8. Red

10. Orange

12. Yellow

15. Green

16. Dark Green

18. Light Blue

19. Blue

22. Violet

4. Brown

12. Yellow

15. Green

17. Aqua Green

19. Blue

22. Violet

23. Pink

24. Vivid Pink

4. Brown

8. Red

10. Orange

12. Yellow

14. Light Green

15. Green

16. Dark Green

17. Aqua Green

22. Violet

1. Black

4. Brown

8. Red

9. Orange Red

10. Orange

12. Yellow

13. Golden Yellow

15. Green

17. Aqua Green

18. Light Blue

20. Dark Blue

21. Lilac

24. Vivid Pink

1. Black

10. Orange

11. Light Yellow

12. Yellow

14. Light Green

15. Green

16. Dark Green

18. Light Blue

19. Blue

24. Vivid Pink

ENJOY BONUS
IMAGES FROM SOME
OF OUR
OTHER FUN
COLOR BY NUMBER
BOOKS!

FIND ALL OF OUR
BOOKS
ON AMAZON

Easy Design
Adult Color By Number
Jumbo Coloring Book of Large Print
Flowers, Birds, and Butterflies

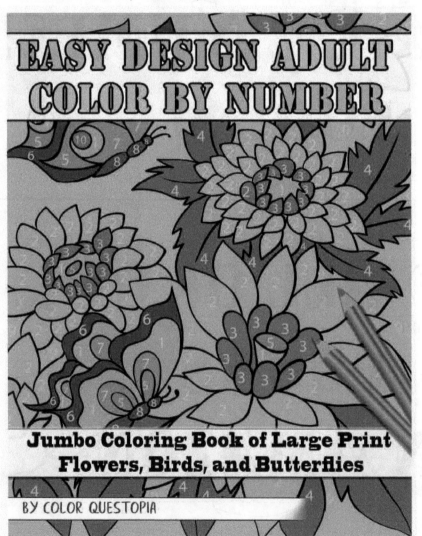

1. Pink   2. Yellow   3. Light Green   4. Red   5. Orange   6. Brown
7. Sky Blue   8. Purple   9. Dark Green

Large Print
Color By Numbers for Adults
Jumbo Coloring Book Of Flowers, Birds, and Butterflies

1. Black

5. Red

9. Yellow

12. Light Orange

14. Orange

23. Medium Green

28. Light Pink

30. Pink

33. Medium Purple

37. Violet

39. Baby Blue

41. Light Blue

SUMMER
Color By Number
Coloring Book for Adults

4. Brown

5. Dark Brown

6. Tan

7. Peach

8. Red

10. Orange

12. Yellow

14. Light Green

15. Green

16. Dark Green

18. Light Blue

20. Dark Blue

23. Pink

24. Vivid Pink

* . Any Flesh Tone

Flowers and Gardens
Color By Number
Coloring Book for Adults

4. Brown

5. Dark Brown

6. Tan

10. Orange

12. Yellow

14. Light Green

15. Green

16. Dark Green

17. Aqua Green

18. Light Blue

20. Dark Blue

21. Lilac

22. Violet

24. Vivid Pink

Inspirational Quotes
Large Print Adult Color By Number Coloring Book for Adults

1. Black

8. Red

9. Orange Red

10. Orange

12. Yellow

13. Golden Yellow

14. Light Green

16. Dark Green

17. Aqua Green

18. Light Blue

19. Blue

20. Dark Blue

21. Lilac

22. Violet

23. Pink

24. Vivid Pink

Custom Color Chart

Medium: _ _ _ _ _ _ _ _   Brand: _ _ _ _ _ _ _ _

1.Black _____   2 .Gray _____   3. Dark Gray _____   4. Brown _____

5.Dark Brown _____   6.Tan _____   7. Peach _____   8.Red _____

9.Orange Red _____   10.Orange _____   11. Light Yellow _____ 12. Yellow _____

13.Golden Yellow _____ 14.Light Green _____ 15. Green _____   16.Dark Green _____

17.Aqua Green _____   18.Light Blue _____ 19. Blue _____   20. Dark Blue _____

21. Lilac _____   22.Violet _____   23.Pink _____   24. Vivid Pink _____

* Flesh Tone _____

Custom Color Chart

Medium: _ _ _ _ _ _ _ _ _   Brand: _ _ _ _ _ _ _ _ _

1. _____

2. _____

3. _____

4. _____

5. _____

6. _____

7. _____

8. _____

9. _____

10. _____

11. _____

*12. _____

13. _____

14. _____

15. _____

16. _____

17. _____

18. _____

19. _____

20. _____

21. _____

22. _____

23. _____

24. _____

* _____

Color Testing Sheet

Color Testing Sheet

Printed in the USA
CPSIA information can be obtained
at www.ICGtesting.com
LVHW050953021023
759880LV00020B/167